grade
3

For full details of exam requirements, please refer to the current syllabus in conjunction with *Examination Information & Regulations* and the guide for candidates, teachers and parents, *These Music Exams*. These three documents are available online at www.abrsm.org, as well as free of charge from music retailers, from ABRSM local representatives or from the Services Department, The Associated

24 Portland Place

GW00381169

CONTENTS AND TRACK LISTING

Track

Where appropriate, pieces in this album have been checked with original source material and edited as necessary for instructional purposes. Fingering, metronome marks and the editorial realization of ornaments (where given) are for guidance only; they are not comprehensive or obligatory.

Editor for the Associated Board: **Richard Jones**

DO NOT PHOTOCOPY © MUSIC

Alternative pieces for this grade

Music origination by Barnes Music Engraving Ltd
Cover by Økvik Design
Printed in England by Headley Brothers Ltd,
The Invicta Press, Ashford, Kent

Menuet in G

BWV Anh. II 116

from *Clavierbüchlein vor Anna Magdalena Bach, 1725*

A:1

ANON.

This minuet is drawn from the second of the two little manuscript keyboard books that J. S. Bach dedicated to his wife Anna Magdalena. The book gives a fascinating portrait of domestic music-making in the Bach family home during the composer's Leipzig period (1723–50). The Menuet in G is one of three anonymous minuets that might have been composed by friends of the family. The dynamics and slurs (except for those of bb. 15 and 23, which are present in the source) are editorial suggestions only. Crotchets might be lightly detached.
Source: *Clavierbüchlein vor Anna Magdalena Bach, 1725*, Staatsbibliothek zu Berlin, Preussischer Kulturbesitz, Mus.ms.Bach P 225

Adapted from J. S. Bach *et al.*: *The Anna Magdalena Bach Book of 1725*, edited by Richard Jones (ABRSM Publishing)

Now is the month of maying

Arranged by
Peter Gritton

T. MORLEY

This piece is a piano arrangement by Peter Gritton of one of the most famous of the five-part balletts by the English composer Thomas Morley (1557/8–1602), drawn from his *First Booke of Balletts To Five Voyces* (London, 1595). The text of the first verse reads:

Now is the month of maying,
When merry lads are playing,
 fa la, etc.
Each with his bonny lass
Upon the greeny grass.
 fa la, etc.

Andante in C

No. 1 from *XII petites pièces*

A:3

attrib. MOZART

This Andante is the first of 12 small piano pieces that were not published until after Mozart's death. Ten of them are piano versions, made by an unknown arranger, of well-known chamber or orchestral movements by the great composer. In two cases, however, including the present Andante, the original remains unidentified. The dynamics and slurs in bb. 1–4 and 17–20 are editorial suggestions only; elsewhere they are mostly original, but with occasional editorial additions.

Source: *XII petites pièces pour le Piano-Forte composées par W. A. Mozart* (Leipzig: C. F. Peters, *c*.1800)

AB 3388

Petit berger

No. 8 from *Du rythme à l'expression*, Book 2, Op. 108

ABSIL

Petit berger Little Shepherd

The Belgian composer Jean Absil (1893–1974) studied at the Brussels Conservatory, where he was later a professor for many years. His piano collection *Du rythme à l'expression*, Op. 108, of 1961, from which this piece is drawn, is designed to aid the study of sonority, rhythm, contrast and expression. 'Petit berger' is a study in colour and sustained phrasing.

Study in F

Op. 65 No. 25

B:2

Edited by
Alan Jones

LOESCHHORN

Andante cantabile [♩ = *c*.104]

Carl Albert Loeschhorn (1819–1905) was a German pianist and composer who studied at the Royal Institute for Church Music, Berlin, where he was later appointed professor of piano. He composed salon pieces, piano sonatas and chamber music, but is known today for his piano studies. The dynamics in the Study in F are editorial suggestions only.

Reproduced from *A Romantic Sketchbook for Piano*, Book II, edited by Alan Jones (ABRSM Publishing)

AB 3388

B:3

L'éléphant

from *Le carnaval des animaux*

Arranged by
Hans-Günter Heumann

SAINT-SAËNS

Le carnaval des animaux The Carnival of the Animals

The French composer, pianist and organist Camille Saint-Saëns (1835–1921) entered the Paris Conservatoire in 1848, where he studied organ and composition. He worked as a church organist in Paris for many years (1853–77) and taught at the École Niedermeyer, where his pupils included Fauré. He composed *Le carnaval des animaux*, subtitled 'grande fantaisie zoologique' (Grand Zoological Fantasy), within a few days while on holiday in Austria in February 1886. It is scored for an unusual chamber ensemble consisting of two pianos, single strings, flute, clarinet, harmonica and xylophone. The fifth of the 14 movements is 'L'éléphant' (originally in E flat major and 3/8 time), in which the creature is represented by solo double bass. With deliberate absurdity, Saint-Saëns has the heavy-footed beast dancing to the 'Ballet des sylphes' from Berlioz's *La damnation de Faust* (see above, bb. 21–4, LH). The movement is given here in a piano arrangement by Hans-Günter Heumann.

Hommage à Prof. Yang Ti-Lie

Tell You

from *Chinese Short Pieces*

C:1

CHOW SHU SAN

This is the fifth of ten short piano pieces by the Hong Kong composer and piano teacher Chow Shu San published in 1973. The composer writes: 'These pieces are truly Chinese in character… I hope that composers of all nationalities will continue to write music bearing the distinctive characteristics of their individual countries. Such music provides excellent material for teachers and young pianists alike.'

Top Cat!

Arranged by
Nicholas Burt

HANNA, BARBERA and CURTIN

The American composer and arranger Hoyt Curtin (1922–2000) is best known as the composer of theme and incidental music to numerous television programmes, including many of the Hanna-Barbera cartoons such as 'The Flintstones', 'Scooby-Doo' and 'Top Cat' (originally renamed 'Boss Cat' for British audiences because a brand of cat food called 'Top Cat' was on sale in the UK). The quavers are to be played swung, except for in the RH of b. 8 where straight quavers should be played.

Quajira

C:3

HOLD

Trevor Hold (1939–2004) was an English composer and poet who read music at Nottingham University and later taught in various university music and adult education departments. He wrote extensively on the subject of English song. 'Quajira' is a variant of 'guajira', a traditional Cuban style of song featuring an alternation between 3/4 and 6/8 time. The repeat should be played in the exam.

8/08